Just Juices

Fruit & Vegetables!

A collection of delicious fruit and vegetable juice drinks!

(im)PulsePaperbacks

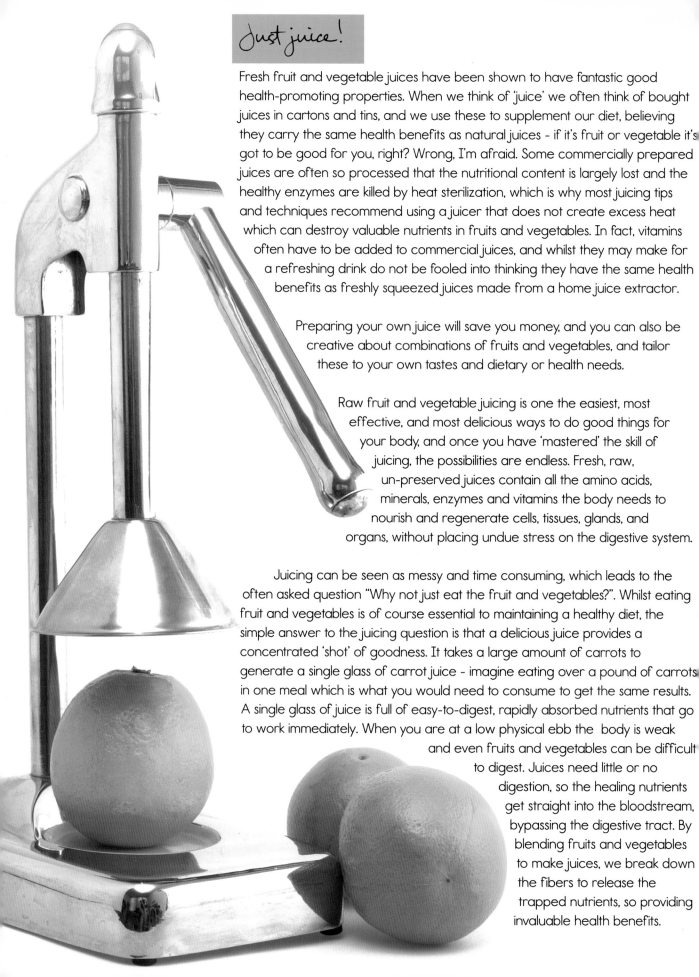

Just juice!

Fresh fruit and vegetable juices have been shown to have fantastic good health-promoting properties. When we think of 'juice' we often think of bought juices in cartons and tins, and we use these to supplement our diet, believing they carry the same health benefits as natural juices - if it's fruit or vegetable it's got to be good for you, right? Wrong, I'm afraid. Some commercially prepared juices are often so processed that the nutritional content is largely lost and the healthy enzymes are killed by heat sterilization, which is why most juicing tips and techniques recommend using a juicer that does not create excess heat which can destroy valuable nutrients in fruits and vegetables. In fact, vitamins often have to be added to commercial juices, and whilst they may make for a refreshing drink do not be fooled into thinking they have the same health benefits as freshly squeezed juices made from a home juice extractor.

Preparing your own juice will save you money, and you can also be creative about combinations of fruits and vegetables, and tailor these to your own tastes and dietary or health needs.

Raw fruit and vegetable juicing is one the easiest, most effective, and most delicious ways to do good things for your body, and once you have 'mastered' the skill of juicing, the possibilities are endless. Fresh, raw, un-preserved juices contain all the amino acids, minerals, enzymes and vitamins the body needs to nourish and regenerate cells, tissues, glands, and organs, without placing undue stress on the digestive system.

Juicing can be seen as messy and time consuming, which leads to the often asked question "Why not just eat the fruit and vegetables?". Whilst eating fruit and vegetables is of course essential to maintaining a healthy diet, the simple answer to the juicing question is that a delicious juice provides a concentrated 'shot' of goodness. It takes a large amount of carrots to generate a single glass of carrot juice - imagine eating over a pound of carrots in one meal which is what you would need to consume to get the same results. A single glass of juice is full of easy-to-digest, rapidly absorbed nutrients that go to work immediately. When you are at a low physical ebb the body is weak and even fruits and vegetables can be difficult to digest. Juices need little or no digestion, so the healing nutrients get straight into the bloodstream, bypassing the digestive tract. By blending fruits and vegetables to make juices, we break down the fibers to release the trapped nutrients, so providing invaluable health benefits.

Fruit or Vegetables?

Fruit and vegetable juices, whilst both delicious and nutritious, act principally in different ways. Fruit juices are the cleansers of the human system, whilst vegetable juices are the builders and regenerators and if you are juicing primarily for health reasons you should try green vegetable juices such as spinach, kale, chard, parsley or broccoli as the base of your juice recipe. Fruit juices, as with fruits, tend to be higher in sugar and lower in nutrients than vegetable juices.

Do not be tempted to combine fruits and vegetables when juicing as they require different digestive processes. There are some exceptions to this, in particular apples which mix with vegetable juices, and can be used in place of carrots to sweeten the mixture if you prefer a sweeter taste. Given their high water content both lettuce and celery can be combined with either fruit or vegetable juice. Vegetables can also be mixed with carbohydrates or animal proteins. Carbohydrates and animal proteins do not mix well together as they stress the digestive system.
Most fruits mix well together, but you should only mix citrus fruits with other citrus fruits, and melons only with other melons.

Juicing tips

Obviously, the only essential ingredient to juicing is a juicer, raw ingredients and water. To start, don't spend a fortune on an expensive juicer - a medium-priced juicer should be more than adequate, although a purely manual juicer will soon see you give up! Most high street stores and supermarkets now have a range of mid priced machines.

Wash the fruits and vegetables thoroughly before juicing and remove damaged portions, if any. Don't be tempted to use fruits or vegetables that are past their best as this will be reflected in the taste. If you wouldn't eat it - don't juice it! Using organic produce wherever possible will add to the nutritional benefits.

Add the stems and leaves of fruit and vegetables to your juicer as a lot of additional nutrients are often contained in these BUT remove the stems and leaves of carrots, as these are toxic. By the same token you can use the seeds of most citrus fruits (lemon, lime, oranges, etc) but do not use apple seeds, as these are toxic.
The skins of oranges and grapefruits are also toxic, but the white pithy part can be added to your juicer as they are a source of vitamin C and bioflavonoids.

Remember that you can add garnish and flavour to your juices with black pepper, salt, lemon juice, parsley and cinnamon.

Juices have been used to help treat a whole range of health problems, and whilst there are few clinical studies on juice therapy, there is strong evidence to support the use of juices in the restoration and maintenance of good health. Juices are a great source of vitamins and minerals.

Vitamins

Vitamins are substances that your body needs to grow and develop normally. There are 13 vitamins your body needs. They are vitamins A, C, D, E, K and the B vitamins (thiamine, riboflavin, niacin, pantothenic acid, biotin, vitamin B-6, vitamin B-12 and folate). You can usually get all your vitamins from the foods you eat. Your body can also make vitamins D and K. People who eat a vegetarian diet may need to take a vitamin B12 supplement. Each vitamin has specific jobs. If you have low levels of certain vitamins, you may develop a deficiency disease. For example, if you don't get enough vitamin D, you could develop rickets. Some vitamins may help prevent medical problems. Vitamin A prevents night blindness. The best way to get enough vitamins is to eat a balanced diet with a variety of foods. In some cases, you may need to take a daily multivitamin for optimal health. However, high doses of some vitamins can make you sick.

Vitamin A

Crucial for the development and maintenance of strong teeth and bones, good vision and healthy skin, (dubbed the anti-ageing vitamin due to it's ability to slow down the skins ageing process).

Vitamin A works with Carotenes, which help the body protect itself from damaging free radicals.

The benefits of Vitamin A are that it enhances the body's immune system, lowers cholesterol levels and assists with hormone production .

Vitamin A is found in the following fruits and vegetables:-

Nectarines, cantaloupes, apricots, kiwi fruit, peaches, blackberries, mandarins, oranges, plums, watermelons, avocado and mangos.

Asparagus, kale, escarole, chicory, endive, romaine lettuce, broccoli, peas, watercress, carrots, green and red pepper, pumpkin, butternut squash, turnips, sweet potato and tomatoes.

Vitamin B1 (Thiamin)

Converts blood sugars into glucose; an important source of energy. Assists the body in breaking down carbohydrates, proteins and fats. The benefits of Vitamin B1 are helping to maintain a healthy functioning of the nervous and cardiovascular system. It also assists healthy muscular function. Produces adenosine triphosphate – the body's major source of fuel, which circulates the blood and boosts energy, mood and concentration levels.

Vitamin B1 is found in the following fruits and vegetables:-

Navy beans, kidney beans, garbanzo beans, peas, avocado, watermelon, oranges, orange juice and raisins.

Vitamin B2 (Riboflavin)

Assists the body in breaking down carbohydrates, proteins and fats. The benefits of Vitamin B2 are assisting the body in the formation of red blood cells and production of antibodies – vital for fighting infection. Benefits skin, nails, hair and connective tissues and assists the production of B3 (Niacin) and absorption of B6.

Vitamin B2 is found in the following fruits and vegetables:-

Leafy green vegetables, avocado, broccoli, asparagus, legumes, mushrooms and kiwi fruit.

Vitamin B3 (Niacin)

Assists the body in breaking down carbohydrates, proteins and fats. Maintains healthy arteries and lowers cholesterol – promoting healthy blood flow. Benefits the nervous system, digestive tract and cognitive functioning. Assists in hormone production.

Vitamin B3 is found in the following fruits and vegetables:-

Green vegetables, turnips, carrots, celery, peas, potatoes, mushrooms, asparagus, artichoke, kale, broccoli, green pepper, peaches, tomatoes, kiwi fruit, bananas and watermelon.

Vitamin B5 (Pantothenic Acid)

Converts carbohydrates, fats and proteins into energy. Stimulates the adrenal glands and vital adrenal hormones. Benefits include increasing stamina and energy and the production of essential antibodies. Vitamin B5 helps with symptoms of stress and anxiety. Lowers cholesterol levels; assists in the prevention and symptoms of arthritis. Maintains healthy skin and hair – used to treat acne and rosacea. Assists the skin's healing process and slows down the skin's ageing process.

Vitamin B5 is found in the following fruits and vegetables:-

Peas, legumes, broccoli, collard greens, bananas, oranges, mushrooms, avocado, sweet potato, corn, lima beans, artichokes, broccoli, cauliflower and carrots.

Vitamin B6 (Pyridoxine)

Assists the production of haemoglobin. Assists in the production of hormones, prostaglandins, enzymes and neurotransmitters; including serotonin the regulator for sleep, mood and appetite. The benefits of Vitamin B6 are that it promotes a healthy immune system and lowers cholesterol.

Vitamin B6 is found in the following fruits and vegetables:-

Bananas, watermelon, carrots, avocados, peas and potatoes.

Vitamin B9 (Folate/Folic Acid)

Assists the body in breaking down carbohydrates, proteins and fats. Assists the body in creating red blood cells, carrying iron and fighting heart disease. It is recommended for women planning to conceive in preventing the foetus developing spinal conditions. Vitamin B9 plays a role in the body's ability to repair damaged tissues and assists in the production of the neurotransmitter, serotonin - the regulator for sleep, mood and appetite.

Aids digestion and may protect against cervical cancer.

Vitamin B9 is found in the following fruits and vegetables:-

Green leafy vegetables such as spinach and asparagus, legumes, lima beans, asparagus, avocado, broccoli, sweet potato, kale, carrots, onions, green peppers, citrus fruits, fruit juices, kiwi fruit, strawberries and bananas.

Vitamin C (Ascorbic Acid)

Works as a powerful antioxidant, fighting the effects of free radicals. Produces collagen, assisting in delaying the skins ageing processes. Vitamin C assists the body's ability to repair tissues quickly and is vital to the process of metabolising folic acid. The benefits of Vitamin C are that it helps the body recover from the effects of colds more quickly, keeps teeth and gums healthy and assists the body's production of red blood cells and haemoglobin.

Vitamin C is found in the following fruits and vegetables:-

Oranges, tangerines, limes, guava, lemons, papayas, strawberries, blackcurrants, blackberries, watermelon, peaches, apples, grapes, grapefruit, mangoes, collard greens, sweet and hot peppers, broccoli, tomatoes, brussel sprouts, cabbage, cucumber, onions, sweet potato, potatoes, kale, spinach, and watercress.

Vitamin D (Calciferol)

Assists the body in absorbing calcium, keeping bones healthy and strong. Reduces the risks of developing osteoporosis and joint damage and is believed to slow down the symptoms of arthritis

Vitamin D is found in the following fruits and vegetables:-

Mushrooms. Not naturally in fruit, orange juice which is fortified with Vitamin D is available.

Vitamin E

Works as an antioxidant, fighting the effects of free radical. Vitamin E helps slow down the ageing process and is believed to help prevent prostate and some other types of cancer. The benefits include lowering cholesterol levels, boosting the immune system and assisting the healthy development of muscles.

Vitamin E is found in the following fruits and vegetables:-

Sweet potatoes, mangoes, apples, bananas, kiwi fruit, blackberries, yams, spinach, broccoli, corn and avocados.

Minerals

It's important to remember that vitamins aren't the only valuable nutrients that can be gained from fruit and vegetables. Minerals are equally as important in keeping our bodies healthy.

Minerals such as potassium, calcium, phosphorous, magnesium, sulphur and chloride are all essential to our diets and can be found in abundance in a wide range of fruits and vegetables. For more information visit an internet resource such as www.vitamins-nutrition.org.

Nutritional Values

Food substance = 100 g.	energy kJ/Kcal	water %	fibre g	fat g	protein g	sugar g	vit.A ug	vit.C mg	vit.B1 mg	vit.B2 mg	vit.B6 mg	vit.E mg
Apple	207/49	84	2.3	0	0.4	11.8	2	15	0.02	0.01	0.05	0.5
Apricot	153/36	87	2.1	0	1.0	8.0	420	5	0.06	0.05	0.06	0.5
Avocado	523/126	81	0.2	10	2.0	7.0	20	17	0.06	0.12	0.36	3.2
Banana	375/88	76	2.7	0	1.2	20.4	3	10	0.04	0.03	0.36	0.3
Blackberry	170/40	85	8.7	0	2.0	8.0	30	150	0.08	0.04	0.07	1.0
Blueberry	204/48	80	8.4	0	1.0	11.0	0	10	0.02	0.03	0.05	1.9
Carrots	48 /11	92	3.3	0	0.6	2.2	312	2	0.03	0.04	0.08	0.2
Cherry	221/52	86	1.2	0	0.0	13.0	40	10	0.02	0.02	0.04	0.1
Cranberry	68 /16	89	4.2	0	0.0	4.0	0	15	0.00	0.01	0.07	0
Date	1275/300	20	7.5	0	2.0	73.0	0	0	0.05	0.10	0.10	0.7
Fig	340/80	80	2.0	0	1.0	19.0	10	3	0.06	0.05	0.11	0
Gooseberry	170/40	88	3.2	0	1.0	9.0	0	30	0.02	0.01	0.08	0.4
Grapefruit, Red	128/30	90	1.4	0	0.9	6.6	0	40	0.07	0.02	0.03	0.5
Grapes	274/64	83	2.2	0	0.6	15.5	0	3	0.03	0.01	0.08	0.6
Guava	306/72	81	5.3	0	1.0	17.0	30	218	0.04	0.04	0.14	0
Kiwi Fruit	168/40	84	2.1	0	1.1	8.8	5	70	0.01	0.02	0.12	1.9
Lemon	51/12	96	1.8	0	0.0	3.0	0	40	0.06	0.02	0.04	0.8
Lime	156/37	91	0.3	0	0.0	7.0	0	140	0.03	0.02	0.08	0
Lychee	323/76	82	1.5	0	1.0	18.0	0	39	0.05	0.05	0	0
Mandarin/Tangerine	177/42	88	1.9	0	0.9	9.5	12	30	0.08	0.03	0.084	0.4
Mango	255/60	84	1.0	0	0.0	15.0	210	53	0.05	0.06	0.13	1.0
Melon, Red Water	153/36	93	0.6	0	1.0	8.0	30	6	0.04	0.05	0.07	0
Melon, cantaloupe	122/29	89	0.6	0	0.9	6.3	7	32	0.05	0.02	0.10	0.2
Orange	198/47	87	1.8	0	1.0	10.6	2	49	0.07	0.03	0.06	0.1
Papaya	136/32	91	0.6	0	0.0	8.0	40	46	0.03	0.04	0.04	0
Passion Fruit	158/37	88	3.3	0.4	2.6	5.8	125	23	0.03	0.12	0	0.5
Peach	151/36	89	1.4	0	1.0	7.9	15	7	0.01	0.02	0.02	0.0
Pear	201/47	86	2.1	0	0.3	11.5	0.0	4	0.01	0.01	0.02	0.1
Red Bell Pepper	119/28	91	2.2	0	1.0	6.0	172	80	0.04	0.14	0.43	6.4
Pineapple	211/50	84	1.2	0	0.4	12.0	20	25	0.07	0.02	0.09	0.1
Pomegranate	343/81	82	3.4	0	1.0	17.0	10	7	0.05	0.02	0.31	0
Plum	177/42	84	2.2	0	0.8	9.6	18	5	0.02	0.03	0.10	0.7
Strawberry	99/23	91	2.2	0	0.7	5.1	10	60	0.02	0.03	0.06	0.4
Tomato	48/11	97	1.4	0	0.9	1.9	140	15	0.05	0.02	0.08	0.7

Source: Nevo table 1996, Nevo Foundation, Netherlands Nutrition Centre

Healing juices

There are certain juices and combination of juices that can have a healing effect on the body.

Condition	Recommended juice
Anemia	Blackberry mixed with parsley juice
Arthritis	Celery mixed with parsley juice
Asthma	Celery mixed with papaya juice
Bladder Ailments	Celery mixed with pomegranate juice
Blood Pressure, high	Carrot mixed with parsley and celery juice
Blood Pressure, low	Parsley juice
Cholesterol Reduction	Mix carrot, apple, orange, strawberry, and spinach juices with ginger
Cold and flu prevention	Apple, carrot, garlic, ginger, lemon
Cold cure	Watercress with apple juice and cream of tartar
Colitis	Coconut milk with carrot juice
Constipation	Spinach and grapefruit juice
Detoxing	Apple, ginger, grapefruit, watermelon
Diarrhea	Blackberry juice with carrot juice
Digestive aid	Apple, beetroot, carrot, ginger
Excessive perspiration	Celery and prune juice
Fever	Celery and parsley juice
Gall Bladder	Prune with black cherry, celery and radish juice
Gas	Coconut milk with carrot juice
Hangover	Apple, beetroot, carrot, orange
Immune System Boost	Apple, carrot, garlic, ginger
Indigestion	Coconut milk with carrot juice, fig juice and parsley
Insomnia	Lettuce and celery juice
Jetlag	Apple, beetroot, carrot, orange
Kidney (bladder) problems	Celery and pomegranate juice
Relaxation enducer	Apple, mint, lime, pineapple
Skin Tonic	Carrot and spinach
Sore Throat	Watercress with apple juice and cream of tartar
Stress reducing	Broccoli, carrot, celery, coriander, tomato
Stomach Infection	Carrot and blackberry juice
Tiredness	Apple, beetroot, carrot, orange

Let's juice!

Now you know some of the health benefits associated with drinking delicious juices, just a few top tips before you begin. Firstly, remember to make your juices delicious - the recipes in this book should be used as a guide, but if you prefer a thinner or thicker consistency adjust the water content accordingly. Also, the softer the raw fruit or vegetable, the thicker the juice will be. Juice extracted from very soft fruits like pears, peaches, strawberries and apricots is often better known as nectar as the texture is much thicker than that of say apple juice.

If you prefer the taste of juice without pulp you can always use a coffee filter as an additional strainer to put your juice through after it has been through your juicer. Remember that juice tastes best when fresh and should be stored no more than 24 hours in a fridge, but if you are making a large amount of juice, i.e from several pounds of fruit and vegetables, be sure to give the juicer a rest and clean out the pulp so that you will not damage your juicer or reduce its effectiveness. If you sip or drink your juice slowly, or with a glass of water, this will allow your body to better digest the nutrients and in general terms you should not eat solid foods at the same time as drinking juices as the juice is a concentrated meal in itself, and the additional stress on your digestion will negate any benefits. Drinking juices is not meant to be a chore to either you or your digestive system, but you can "overdose" if your body is not used to them, so go easy at first.

You could begin with carrot juice as this is the base of many juicing combinations. Carrot juice is a powerful blood cleaner, and unlike other vegetable juices is easy to drink straight. Try adding other ingredients over a period of time. Here are a few suggestions:

Celery – contains a high amount of vital organic sodium. It's also good in combination with cucumber.

Cucumber – contains silica, potassium and magnesium, and improves the complexion and health of the skin.

Garlic – a wonderful heart strengthener and toner.

Ginger – helps soothe and improve digestion.

Lettuce – Romaine especially is nutritionally packed.

Parsley – a rich source of antioxidant and cardio-protective nutrients. Parsley is great for increasing oxygen to the brain, which can help improve memory.

Potato – a nutrient-dense food, high in potassium when consumed raw.

Spinach – another powerful blood cleanser.

Sunny delight

4 carrots
3 oranges

Directions

Process through a juicer and serve.

Luscious lemon delight

1 lemon
2 sticks of celery
3 carrots

Directions

Process through a juicer and serve.

Muddy marvel

3 carrots
1 orange
5 large kale leaves

Directions

Process through a juicer and serve.

Flavoursome fruit twist

1 pear
1 apple
1 orange
2 carrots
1 thick slice of watermelon

Directions

Process through a juicer and serve.

Marvellous mango surprise

1 mango
3 carrots
1/2 orange
1 stick of celery

Directions

Process through a juicer and serve.

Cool as a cucumber

1 cucumber
3 carrots

Directions

Process through a juicer and serve.

Joint Soother

3 carrots
1 inch giner root
1/2 pineapple
1 tsp of linseed oil

Directions

Process through a juicer and serve.

Vegetable delight

2 carrots
1 red pepper
1 spear of broccoli
1/2 sweet potato

Directions

Process through a juicer and serve.

Crazy carrot juice

4 carrots
1 handful of watercress
1 bunch of parsley
1 lime

Directions

Process through a juicer and serve.

Carradish Juice

1 handful of radishes
4 medium-sized carrots
4 tomatoes
salt and pepper to taste

Directions

Process through a juicer and serve.

Carrot sunrise

2 carrots
1 apple
1 peach
1 handful of raspberries

Directions

Process through a juicer and serve.

Carrot Munch Bunch

1 orange
4 carrots
1 bunch of fresh parsley

Directions

Process through a juicer and serve.

Taste of heaven

carrots
apples
sweet potato
prinkle of fresh mint

Directions

rocess through a juicer and serve.

Fresh breath fix

handful of parsley
medium-sized carrots

Directions

rocess through a juicer and serve.

Carrot and salad surprise

tomatoes
stick of celery
carrots
/2 lime

Directions

rocess through a juicer and serve.

Scrummy celery and beetroot

2 carrots
2 beetroots
1 apple
1 stick of celery
1/2 inch ginger root

Directions

Process through a juicer and serve.

Digestion soother

1/2 pineapple
2 pears
2 carrots
1/2 inch ginger root

Directions

Process through a juicer and serve.

Apple and orange explosion

2 oranges
2 apples

Directions

Process through a juicer and serve.

Apple and grape attack

1 nectarine
1 bunch of red grapes
3 apples

Directions

Process through a juicer and serve.

Apple and cherry juice

2 apples
2 handfuls of cherries

Directions

Process through a juicer and serve.

Fruit shoot

2 pears
1 apple
1/2 lemon
1/2 pineapple

Directions

Process through a juicer and serve.

Sunset Boulevard

2 peaches
1 nectarine
1 apple
1 handful of raspberries

Directions

Process through a juicer and serve.

Apple Crumble

2 handfuls of blackberries
2 apples

Directions

Process through a juicer and serve.

Dreamy apple delight

2 apples
4 sticks of celery

Directions

Process through a juicer and serve.

Apple Cinnamon Stick

1 cinnamon stick
2 apples

Directions

Process apples through a juicer, place cinnamon stick in juice and chill for 1 hour. Remove cinnamon stick and serve.

Apple time

2 apples
1/2 pineapple
1/2 fennel bulb

Directions

Process through a juicer and serve.

Apple dapple juice

2 apples
3 sprigs of fresh mint
3 sticks of celery
1 handful of cranberries
1/2 inch ginger root

Directions

Process through a juicer and serve.

Tropical Apple Thunder

apple
guavas
cucumber
/2 orange

Directions

Process through a juicer and serve.

Tangy tomato juice

8 tomatoes
1 stick of celery
1/2 lemon
1 tsp of Tabasco
1 tsp of salt

Directions

Process through a juicer and serve.

Red white and blue combo

6 tomatoes
1 handful of blueberries
1 apple

Directions

Process through a juicer and serve.

Tomato top-up

6 tomatoes
1/4 long cucumber
1/2 ginger root
1 handful of mint, chopped
1 lime

Directions

Process through a juicer and serve.

Tomato and parsley paradise

1 lemon
6 tomatoes
1 large bunch of parsley
salt and pepper to taste

Directions

Process through a juicer and serve.

Tasty tomato treat

5 tomatoes
1 bunch of parsley
1 lemon

Directions

Process through
a juicer and
serve.

Tangy tomato salad

4 tomatoes
1 small sprig of fresh mint
1 cucumber
1 small kiwi
1/2 lemon

Directions

Process through a juicer and serve.

Tomato and cucumber combo

1/2 long cucumber
4 tomatoes
2 broccoli spears
1 large handful of spinach leaves

Directions

Process through a juicer and serve.

Raspberry bonanza

2 handfuls of raspberries
1 handful of blueberries
1 handful of blackberries
6 strawberries

Directions

Process through a juicer and serve.

Berry Blend

1 handful of blackberries
1 handful of raspberries
1 apple

Directions

Process through a juicer and serve.

Raspberry Tang

2 large handfuls of raspberries
1 grapefruit
1/2 lemon
1/2 lime

Directions

Process through a juicer and serve.

Tropical Kiwi

1 guava
2 kiwis
2 pears
1/2 watermelon

Directions

Process through a juicer and serve.

Kiss-me Kiwi

2 kiwis
2 pears
2 guavas

Directions

Process through a juicer and serve.

Kiwi Kick

1 kiwi
1 guava
2 grapefruits

Directions

Process through a juicer and serve.

Peach punch

 peaches
 tangerines

Directions

Process through a juicer and serve.

Perfect peach juice

 peach
 grapefruits
 thick slice of melon

Directions

Process through a juicer and serve.

Melonaide

 slices of melon
 peach
 1/2 lemon

Directions

Process through a juicer and serve.

Georgeous Grapefruit

2 grapefruits
1 handful of watercress
1 bunch of parsley

Directions

Process through a juicer and serve.

Sweet Grapefruit Surprise

2 mangoes
2 grapefruits

Directions

Process through a juicer and serve.

Back to basics

1 grapefruit
1 stick of celery
1 apple

Directions

Process through a juicer and serve.

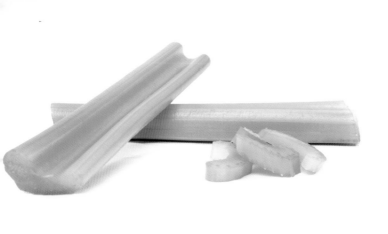

Morning Glory

1 grapefruit
2 sticks of celery
1/2 inch ginger root

Directions

Process through a juicer and serve.

Green Machine

1 grapefruit
2 sticks of celery
2 handfuls of spinach
4 large kale leaves

Directions

Process through a juicer and serve.

Green Giant

8 spears of broccoli
3 sticks of celery
2 pears
1 handful of mint

Directions

Process through a juicer and serve.

The "beet-le"

1 beetroot
1/2 pineapple

Directions

Process through a juicer and serve.

Beet box

4 carrots
2 beetroots
2 oranges

Directions

Process through a juicer and serve.

Beetastic!

2 carrots
1 apple
2 beetroots
1 stick of celery
1 orange
1/2 inch ginger root

Directions

Process through a juicer and serve.

Sergeant Pepper

2 oranges
1/2 red pepper
1/2 yellow pepper
1 kale leaf

Directions

Process through a juicer and serve.

Perfect pepper pick-up

1 yellow pepper
1 red pepper
3 carrots

Directions

Process through a juicer and serve.

Spear of destiny

1 spear of broccoli
1 red pepper
3 carrots
1/2 sweet potato

Directions

Process through a juicer and serve.

Refreshing cucumber lift

2 pears
1 cucumber

Directions

Process through a juicer and serve.

Cucumber Cooler

2 apples
1 cucumber

Directions

Process through a juicer and serve.

Cucumber Mumba

3 tomatoes
1 cucumber
1/2 lemon
1 small bunch of parsley

Directions

Process through a juicer and serve.

Super strawberry surprise

8 strawberries
3 apples
1 nectarine

Directions

Process through a juicer and serve.

Tangy tangerine treat

2 tangerines
2 grapefruits

Directions

Process through a juicer and serve.

Pear perfection

2 pears
1 orange

Directions

Process through a juicer and serve.

Melon medley

1 thick slice of melon
1 thick slice of watermelon
1 small bunch of fresh mint

Directions

Process through a juicer and serve.

Gorgeous grape juice

1 handful of red grapes
1 handful of green grapes
1/2 grapefruit

Directions

Process through a juicer and serve.

Double apricot dream

4 apricots
2 pears

Directions

Process through a juicer and serve.

Cherry and citrus blast

2 large handfuls of cherries
1/2 lime
1/2 lemon

Directions

Process through a juicer and serve.

Mind-blowing mango juice

4 mangoes
1 apple
1 handful of grapes

Directions

Process through a juicer and serve.

Pineapple Express

1 lime
1 pineapple

Directions

Process through a juicer and serve.

Pineapple Cherry Combo

1/2 pineapple
2 large handfuls of cherries

Directions

Process through a juicer and serve.

Zingy Pineapple Juice

1 pineapple
1 lime
1 lemon

Directions

Process through a juicer and serve.

Ginger Zinger

1/2 pineapple
1 inch ginger root

Directions

Process through a juicer and serve.

Grapefruit Mango Gang

2 grapefruits
2 mangoes
1 small bunch of fresh mint

Directions

Process through a juicer and serve.

Gorgeous Grape juice

1 bunch of red grapes
1 nectarine
2 apples

Directions

Process through a juicer and serve.

Watermelon wonder

2 grapefruits
1 thick slice of watermelon

Directions

Process through a juicer and serve.

Peaches and dream

2 peaches
1 nectarine
1/2 watermelon

Directions

Process through a juicer and serve.

Pearberry Passion

1 handful of blackberries
1 handful of blueberries
2 pears

Directions

Process through a juicer and serve.

Pink drink

1 handful of strawberries
1/2 pineapple
1 handful of blackberries

Directions

Process through a juicer and serve.

Blue pear perfection

1 handful of blueberries
3 pears

Directions

Process through a juicer and serve.

Strawberry blush

3 oranges
1 handful of strawberries
1 guava

Directions

Process through a juicer and serve.

Very berry juice

2 handfuls of either raspberries or strawberries
3 apples

Directions

Process through a juicer
and serve.

The recipes contained in this book are passed on in good faith but the publisher cannot be held responsible for any adverse results. Spoon measurements are level, teaspoons are assumed to be 5ml, tablespoons 15ml.

Spoons to millilitres

1/2 teaspoon	2.5 ml	1 Tablespoon	15 ml
1 teaspoon	5 ml	2 Tablespoons	30 ml
1-1 1/2 teaspoons	7.5 ml	3 Tablespoons	45 ml
2 teaspoons	10 ml	4 Tablespoons	60 ml

Grams to ounces

10g	0.25oz	225g	8oz
15g	0.38oz	250g	9oz
25g	1oz	275g	10oz
50g	2oz	300g	11oz
75g	3oz	350g	12oz
110g	4oz	375g	13oz
150g	5oz	400g	14oz
175g	6oz	425g	15oz
200g	7oz	350g	16oz

Metric to cups

Description		1 cup
Flour etc	115g	1 cup
Clear honey etc	350g	1 cup
Liquids etc	225ml	1 cup

Liquid measures

5fl oz	1/4 pint	150 ml
7.5fl oz		215 ml
10fl oz	1/2 pint	275 ml
15fl oz		425 ml
20fl oz	1 pint	570 ml
35fl oz		1 litre

This edition first published in 2009 by ImPulse Paperbacks, an imprint of Iron Press Ltd. © Iron Press Ltd 2009 Printed in China